Language Tree

Workbook 1

Second Edition

macmillan
education

Macmillan Education Ltd
4 Crinan Street
London, N1 9XW

Companies and representatives throughout the world

www.macmillan-caribbean.com

ISBN 978-0-230-48142-8

This edition published 2016
First edition published 2006

Designed by Lucy Allen Graphic Design
Illustrated by Nigel Dobbyn, Tamara Joubert and Claire Mumford c/o Beehive; Dave Hill, Jennifer Kalis and Lisa Williams c/o Sylvie Poggio; Chantel Kees; Tek-Art and Jim Weaver
Cover design by Macmillan Education and Clare Webber
Cover illustration by Nathalie Gavet
Typeset by Jim Weaver

The author and publishers would like to thank the following education professionals for their valuable contributions to this edition:
Suzette Abbott-King (*St Vincent*), Leonie Alexander-Charles (*St Vincent*), Ingrid Daniel-Simon (*Antigua*), Janelle Little (*Barbados*), Tessa McQuilkin (*Grenada*), Christina Morris (*Barbados*), Rochelle Richards (*Antigua*), Edwina Riviere (*Dominica*), Carla St. Louis (*Grenada*) and Sandra Thomas (*Grenada*)

Printed and bound in the UK by CPI Colour Ltd

2025 2024 2023 2022 2021
17 16 15 14 13 12 11 10 9

Contents

How to Use this Book

Language Tree Workbook 1 provides practice in a wide range of reading, writing and comprehension skills required by students in the early years of school.

Workbook 1 can be used alongside *Language Tree Student's Book 1* to reinforce skills. Use the Skills Index at the end of this workbook in combination with the teacher's notes at the bottom of each page in *Student's Book 1* to plan your teaching. Depending on students' level of ability, explore the workbook Exercises with the whole class, or allow students to work independently. Alternatively, set activities for homework, or use them for revision.

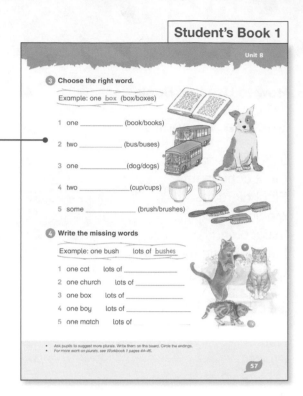

Student's Book 1

Unit 8

3 Choose the right word.

Example: one <u>box</u> (box/boxes)

1 one _____ (book/books)
2 two _____ (bus/buses)
3 one _____ (dog/dogs)
4 two _____ (cup/cups)
5 some _____ (brush/brushes)

4 Write the missing words

Example: one bush ___ lots of <u>bushes</u>

1 one cat   lots of _____
2 one church   lots of _____
3 one box   lots of _____
4 one boy   lots of _____
5 one match   lots of

• Ask pupils to suggest more plurals. Write them on the board. Circle the endings.
• For more work on plurals, see Workbook 1 pages 44–46.

57

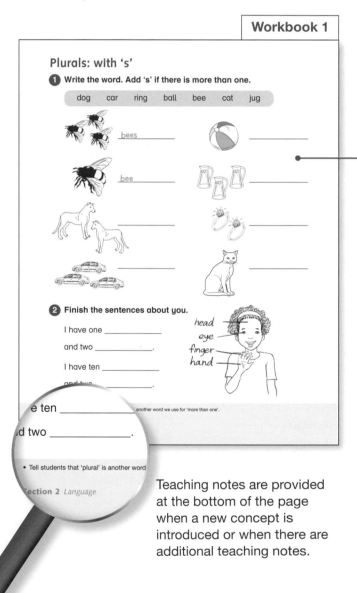

Workbook 1

Plurals: with 's'

1 Write the word. Add 's' if there is more than one.

dog   car   ring   ball   bee   cat   jug

bees

bee

2 Finish the sentences about you.

I have one _____
and two _____.
I have ten _____

head
eye
finger
hand

e ten _____ another word we use for 'more than one'.

d two _____.

• Tell students that 'plural' is another word

ection 2 *Language*

Teaching notes are provided at the bottom of the page when a new concept is introduced or when there are additional teaching notes.

Workbook 1 can also be used independently:

• to improve students' competence in the early years
• to teach and practise important literacy skills alongside any language arts programme.

We recommend that you introduce each skill in context. For example, point out examples of plurals or joining words in *Student's Book 1* or in any story, poem or passage that you are reading with the student.

Additional teaching tips are provided at the bottom of the page when a new concept is introduced or when there are additional teaching tips.

When students are familiar with the concept, use the exercises in the workbook to give extra practice. Explain the exercise and work through the first example together, making sure that students understand what to do. They may then go on to work independently, or with a partner, writing their answers. If they are working independently, monitor their work and offer help where it is needed.

Some of the comprehension exercises are for discussion – thus practising speaking skills as well as comprehension.

Section 1 Phonics

Initial consonants

1 **Write the beginning sound.**

| f | m | h | c |

2 **Write the beginning sound.**

| t | r | d | g |

• Ask students to think of other words that begin with the letters on this page and the following pages.
Remember to say the sound of the letter, not the name.

3 Write the beginning sound.

a b c d e f g h i j k l m n o p q r s t u v w x y z

_u_   _ _   q _   _ _

4 **Write the first letter for each word.**

1 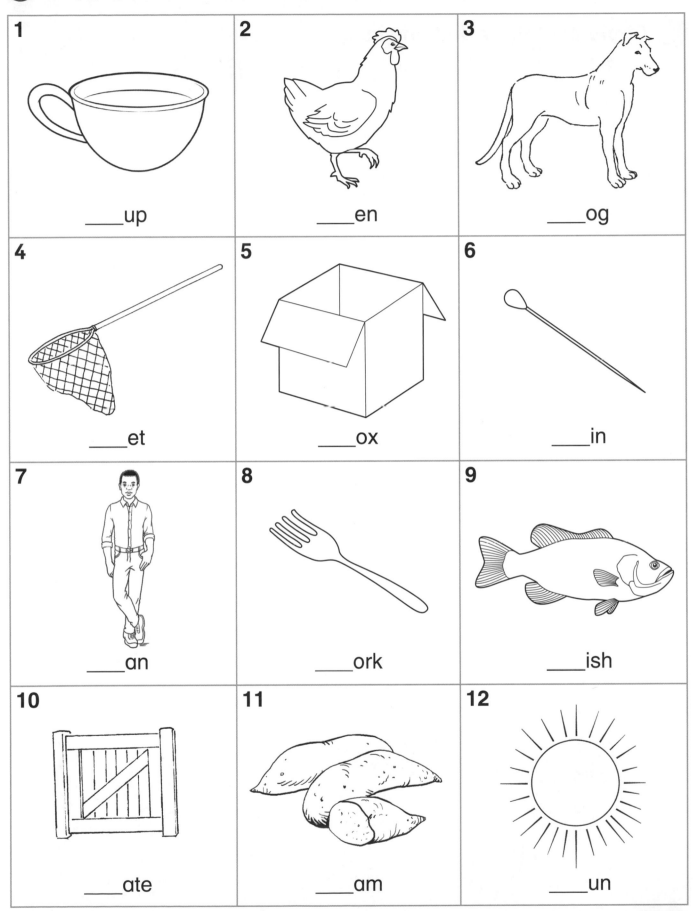 ___up	**2** ___en	**3** ___og
4 ___et	**5** ___ox	**6** ___in
7 ___an	**8** ___ork	**9** ___ish
10 ___ate	**11** ___am	**12** ___un

Final consonants

1 Circle the things that end in 'g'.

2 Circle the things that end in 't'.

3 **Circle the things that end in 'n'.**

4 **Circle the things that end in 'p'.**

5 **Say the words. Circle the word that ends with the same sound as the thing in the box.**

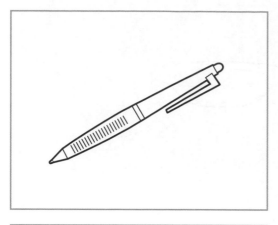

bin   peg   big

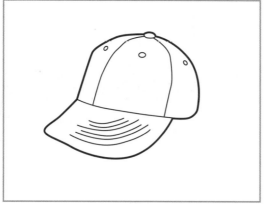

cat   but   top

nod   big   dot

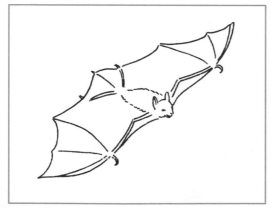

bad   hit   hid

6 **Write the last letter of each word.**
Colour the pictures that end in 'n'.

ha_t___

te____

ca____

fa____

pi____

ma____

be____

le____

su____

ti____

we____

he____

Final digraph: words that end in 'ck'

1 **Make words that end in 'ick' and 'ock'.**

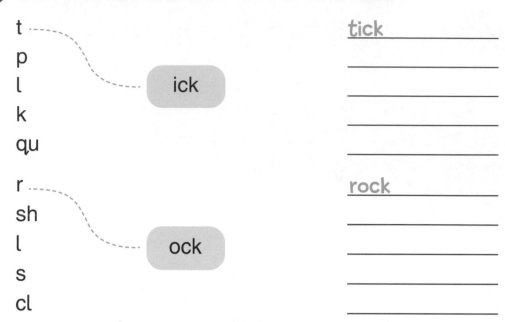

t
p
l
k
qu

ick

r
sh
l
s
cl

ock

tick _____

_____

_____

_____

_____

rock _____

_____

_____

_____

_____

2 **Finish the sentences. Use words from the box.**

sock   lock   kick   clock   lick

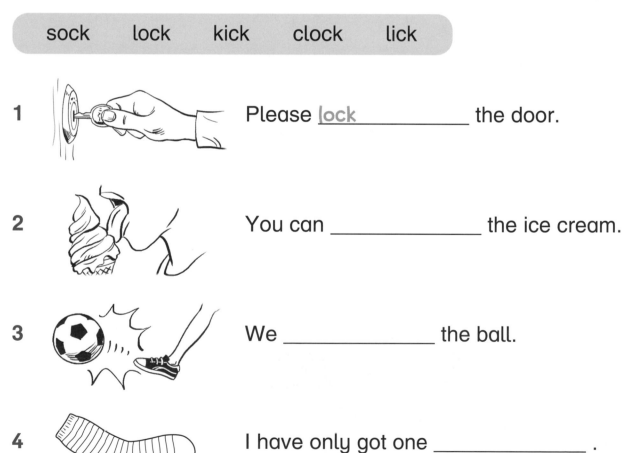

1   Please lock _____ the door.

2   You can _____ the ice cream.

3   We _____ the ball.

4   I have only got one _____ .

Final digraph: words that end in 'ss'

1 Write words ending in 'ss'.

me____ ____

cro____ ____

ki____ ____

ble____ ____

ss

dre____ ____

gra____ ____

2 Finish these sentences. Use a word ending in 'ss'.

1 Anna has a new pink _____ .

2 Good night, God _____ .

3 I gave Mommy a goodbye _____ .

4 My bedroom is a _____ .

Final digraph: words that end in 'll'

1 **Make words ending in 'ell'.**

t - - - - - - - - - - - - _tell_ _____

b _____

sh _____

I am w _____

2 **Make words ending in 'ill'.**

w _____

m _____

st _____

3 **Finish the words in these sentences. Use 'ill' or 'ell'.**

1 Stand st_____ when the b_____ rings.

2 T_____ Auntie that Mommy is w_____ .

3 I will find a pretty sh_____ at the beach.

Final digraph: words that end in 'ng'

1 **Write the words ending in 'ng'.**

_____

_____

ing

_____

_____

2 **Finish these sentences. Use a word ending in 'ng'.**

1 I like to _____ songs in Church.

2 The bird has two big _____.

3 The _____ has a gold crown.

4 Mom has a gold _____.

Final digraph: words that end in 'mp'

1 Add 'amp' or 'ump' to finish these words.

1  I can j_____ over the box.

2  I fell with a b_____ .

3 Turn on the l_____ .

4  I need a st_____ for this letter.

2 Find these 'mp' words in the word puzzle.

jump	bump	camp	stamp	limp

h	j	u	m	p	g	s
c	a	m	p	y	a	t
s	l	r	b	g	u	a
d	i	b	u	m	p	m
p	m	d	t	x	m	p
k	p	w	c	f	h	v

Final digraph: words that end in 'nk' and 'nd'

1 **Use 'nd' to finish these words.**

ba___ ___   ha___ ___   sa___ ___

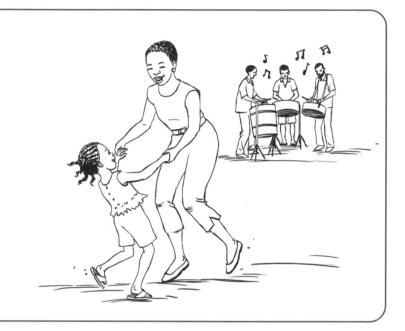

2 **Use the words to complete this rhyme.**

Mommy held my

_____ .

We danced on the

_____

to the music of the

_____ .

3 **Find these 'nk' words in the word puzzle.**

think   pink   bank   drink   tank

g	t	h	a	d
p	i	n	k	r
t	h	i	r	i
h	p	t	g	n
i	b	a	n	k
n	h	n	o	t
k	e	k	r	s

Medial vowels

1 **Write the missing letter**

a e i o u

b_o_x

n___t

c___p

p___n

j___g

v___n

s___x

b___d

m___p

2 **Write the missing letter. Draw a picture.**

This h___n lays eggs.

3 **Choose a word to finish each sentence.**

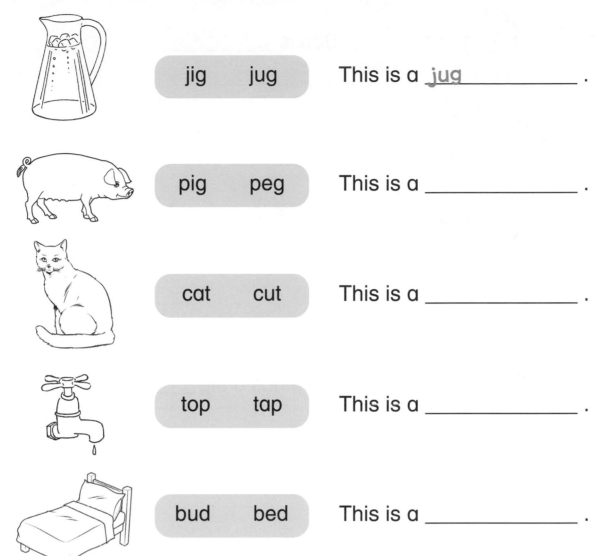

jig   jug   This is a _jug_____ .

pig   peg   This is a _____ .

cat   cut   This is a _____ .

top   tap   This is a _____ .

bud   bed   This is a _____ .

4 **Draw a bad dog.**

Write about your picture.

_____

_____

_____

_____

_____

5 **Finish these sentences.**

1  Ben is <u>six</u>_____ .

2  Pam is in _____ .

3  Mom has a big _____ .

4  I pat the _____ .

5  Dad has a _____ .

Initial blends and digraphs: 'sh'

1 **Complete these words using 'sh'.**

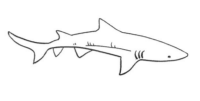

<u>s</u> <u>h</u> op   ___ ___ip   ___ ___y   ___ ___ark

2 **Complete this sentence with two 'sh' words.**

I saw a _____ and a _____ in the sea.

Initial blends and digraphs: 'ch'

1 **Complete these words using 'ch'.**

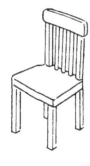

___ ___air   ___ ___urch   ___ ___icken   ___ ___ild

2 **Complete this sentence with two 'ch' words.**

The _____ sat on a

_____ .

Initial blends and digraphs: 'th'

1 **Read aloud what each person says.**

2 **Finish these sentences. Use a word from the box.**

| thin | third | thirty | three |

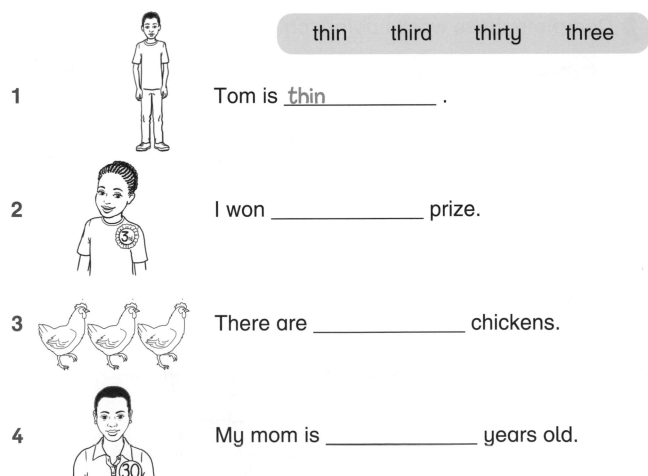

1   Tom is _thin_____ .

2   I won _____ prize.

3   There are _____ chickens.

4   My mom is _____ years old.

Initial blends and digraphs: 'sl' and 'cl'

1 **Make words using 'sl' or 'cl'.**

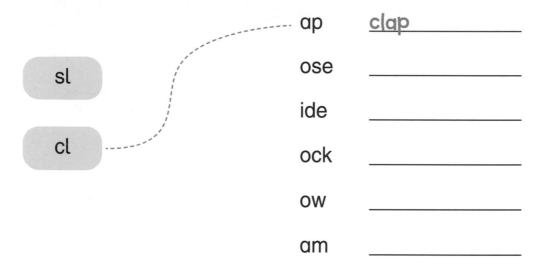

	ap	<u>clap</u>
sl	ose	_____
	ide	_____
cl	ock	_____
	ow	_____
	am	_____

2 **Use one of your words in a sentence.**

_____

3 **Finish the words with 'sl' or 'cl'.**

1   You are a ____ ____ever boy.

2   I want to go to ____ ____eep.

3   There are ____ ____ouds in the sky.

Initial blends and digraphs: 'fl' and 'pl'

1 **Complete the names of these things.**

___ ____ower

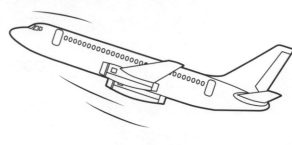

___ ____ane

___ ____ant

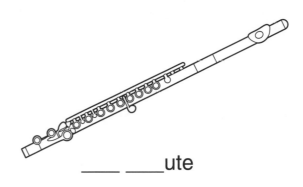

___ ____ute

2 **Make as many words as you can.**

ag

at

pl .... an

ot

fl

ap

ug

plan _____ _____

_____ _____

_____ _____

Initial blends and digraphs: 'br' and 'tr'

1 **Make words using 'br' and 'tr'.**

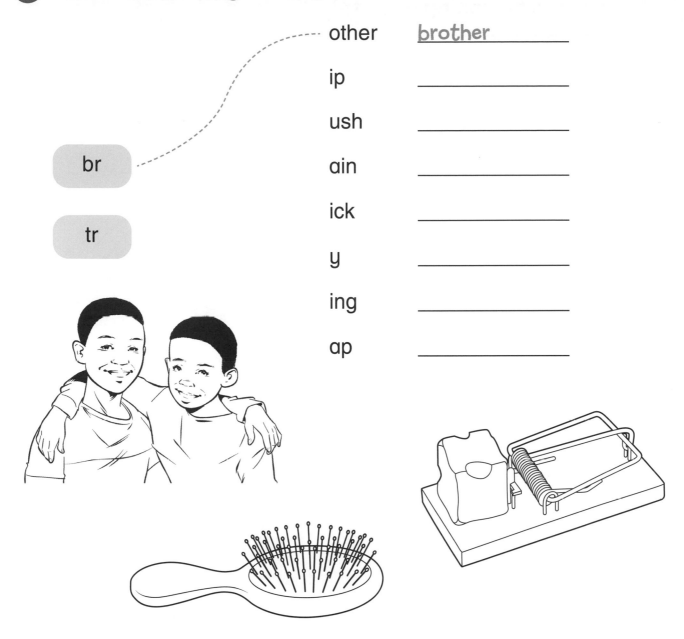

other   <u>brother</u> _____

br

tr

ip   _____

ush   _____

ain   _____

ick   _____

y   _____

ing   _____

ap   _____

2 **Use one of your 'br' words in a sentence.**

_____

3 **Use one of your 'tr' words in a sentence.**

_____

Initial blends and digraphs: 'sn' and 'st'

1 **Make words beginning with 'sn'.**

sn	
ow	snow
ail	
ake	
eeze	
ore	

2 **Make words beginning with 'st'.**

st	
art	
op	
ep	
ill	
ore	

3 **Use one of your new words in a sentence.**

_____

Initial blends and digraphs: review

1 **Match the beginning sounds with the word endings.**

br   ar

tr   ush

sn   ee

pl   ail

st   ate

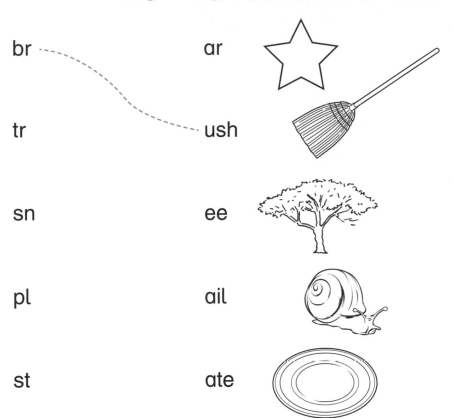

2 **Finish these rhymes with words from the box.**

snake   stop   still

My dog is ill.

He must sit

_____ .

Watch out for the

_____ .

It is in the lake.

I love to hop

I don't want to

_____ .

Long vowels: magic 'e'

1 **Add 'a' and 'e' to make a word with a long 'A' sound.**

c_a_ k _e_   cake _____

sn___k___   _____

r___k___   _____

g___t___   _____

pl___t___   _____

g___m___   _____

2 **Complete the sentences. Use a word from Exercise 1.**

1  I saw a _____ by the tree.

2 I played a _____ with my brother.

3 I eat off a _____.

4 We made a chocolate _____.

3 **Look at the example. Write the words.**

pip + e = pipe

rid + e = _ride_

kit + e = _____

hid + e = _____

rip + e = _____

4 **Use a word with a long 'i' sound in each sentence.**

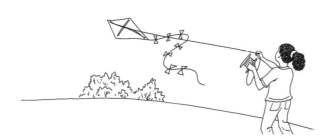

1 I like to fly my

_____ .

2 I ate a _____

of mango.

3 I can _____

under the bed.

4 I can _____

a bike.

5 **Add 'o' and 'e' to make a word with a long 'o' sound.**

h___l___   hole_____

b___n___   _____

st___n___   _____

st___l___   _____

r___p___   _____

h___m___   _____

6 **Complete the sentences. Use a word from the box.**

| stone | bone | hole | stole |

 **1**   A thief _____ my bag.

 **2**   The worm was under a _____.

 **3**   The dog dug a _____.

4   The dog put his _____ in the hole.

7 Say the words below. Add an 'e' to the end of each to make a new word.

Say the new word.

old word	+ e	new word
cub		cube
hat		
bit		
cut		
not		
kit		
tap		

8 Think of a word that rhymes with each of the words below.

bake ___ ___ ___ ___

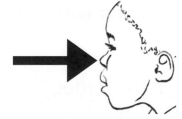

rose ___ ___ ___ ___

nice ___ ___ ___ ___

Long vowel digraph: 'ai'

1 **Finish these words using 'ai'.**

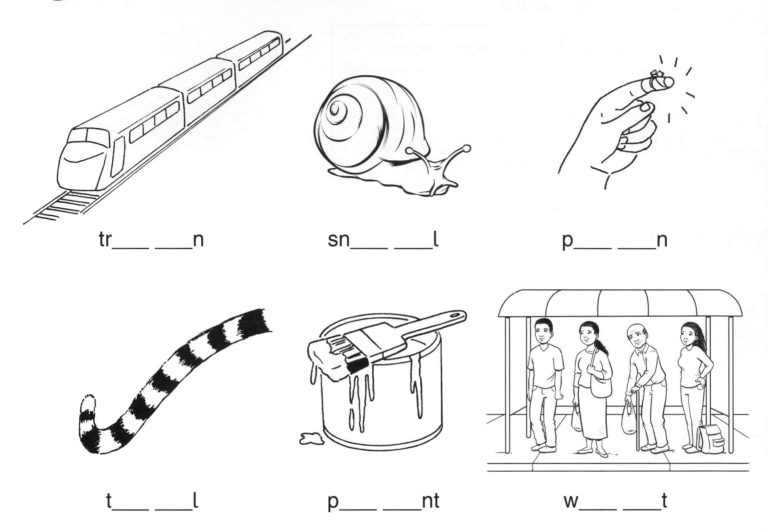

tr___ ___n   sn___ ___l   p___ ___n

t___ ___l   p___ ___nt   w___ ___t

2 **Finish the questions with 'ai' words.**

Then answer the questions with 'Yes' or 'No'.

	Yes	No
1 Did it r___ ___n yesterday?	_____	_____
2 Do you like sn___ ___ls?	_____	_____
3 Did you p___ ___nt a picture yesterday?	_____	_____
4 Are you in p___ ___n?	_____	_____

Long vowel digraph: 'ay'

1 **Read the poem. Underline the words which contain 'ay'.**

It is raining <u>today</u>.

Will the rain stay?

Hooray! Hooray!

Now the rain has gone away.

It is a nice day.

We can go out to play!

2 **Write the 'ay' words below.**

today _____   _____

_____   _____

_____   _____

3 **Write two new words that rhyme with 'day' and 'play'.**

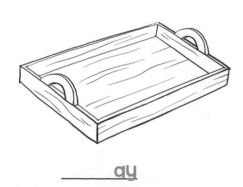

_____ay

_____ay

Long vowel digraphs: 'ai' and 'ay'

1 **How do we make the long 'a' sound?**
Choose 'ai' or 'ay' to finish these words.

t_a__i_l

pr____ ____

p____ ____nt

tr____ ____

pl____ ____

sn____ ____l

2 **Find these words in the word puzzle.**
Draw a ring round each one.

s	a	y	p	u	f
a	y	k	r	y	d
m	o	s	a	i	l
a	w	a	y	m	t
i	b	r	s	g	y
l	c	h	a	i	n

sail
chain
mail
pray
away
say

Long vowel digraph: 'ee'

1 **Finish these words using 'ee'.**

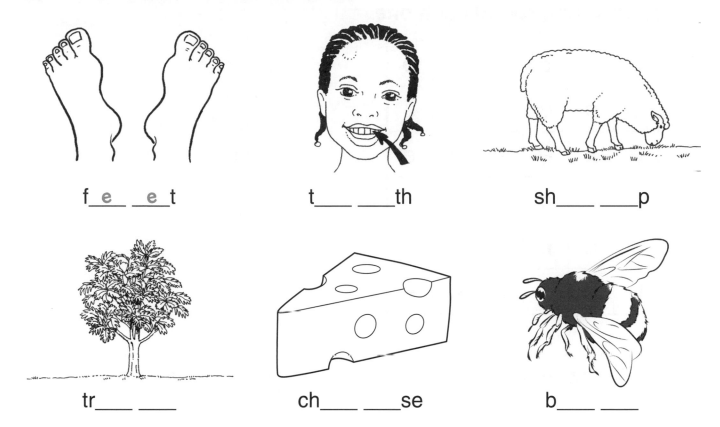

f_e_ _e_t

t___ ___th

sh___ ___p

tr___ ___

ch___ ___se

b___ ___

2 **Answer these riddles. The answers all contain 'ee'.**

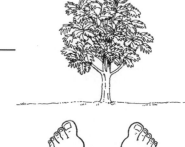

1   It makes honey.   ___ ___ ___

2   It has a trunk and leaves.   ___ ___ ___ __

3   You have two on the

    end of your legs.   ___ ___ ___ ___

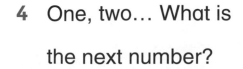

4   One, two… What is

    the next number?   thr___ ___

Long vowel digraph: 'ea'

1 Find these words in the word puzzle.
Draw a ring round each one.

b	e	a	n	j	b
t	s	b	v	s	e
e	x	e	k	e	a
a	r	a	m	a	c
c	u	k	i	t	h
h	s	p	e	a	k

teach
speak
bean
seat
beak
beach

2 Write the word which rhymes with each of the words below.

leak _____

each _____

seat _____

3 Think of a word which rhymes with each of these words.

mean   b___ ___ ___

teach   b___ ___ ___ ___

Long vowel digraphs: 'ea' and 'ee'

1 **Finish the words in the rhyme with 'ea'.**

Let's have t____ ____

By the s____ ____.

Cake and ice cr____ ____m

It's like a dr____ ____m.

Lots to ____ ____t

What a tr____ ____t!

2 **Finish the words in the rhyme with 'ee'.**

Can you s____ ____

The big b____ ____

In the tr____ ____?

3 **Make two lists of words and learn how to spell them.**

words with 'ee'	words with 'ea'
_____	_____
_____	_____
_____	_____
_____	_____

Long vowel digraph: 'oa'

1 **Finish these words using 'oa'.**

b<u>o</u> <u>a</u> t

r____ ____d

g____ ____t

cr____ ____k

c____ ____t

fl____ ____t

2 **Use one of the words from Exercise 1 to finish each sentence.**

1 My ___boat___ sails on the sea.

2 We drive down the _____.

3 I have a red _____.

4 The _____ lives in the field.

5 I can hear the _____ of a frog.

Long vowel digraph: 'oo'

1 Say the words. If it has a long 'oo' as in 'pool' colour it blue.
If it has a short 'oo' as in 'look' colour it red.

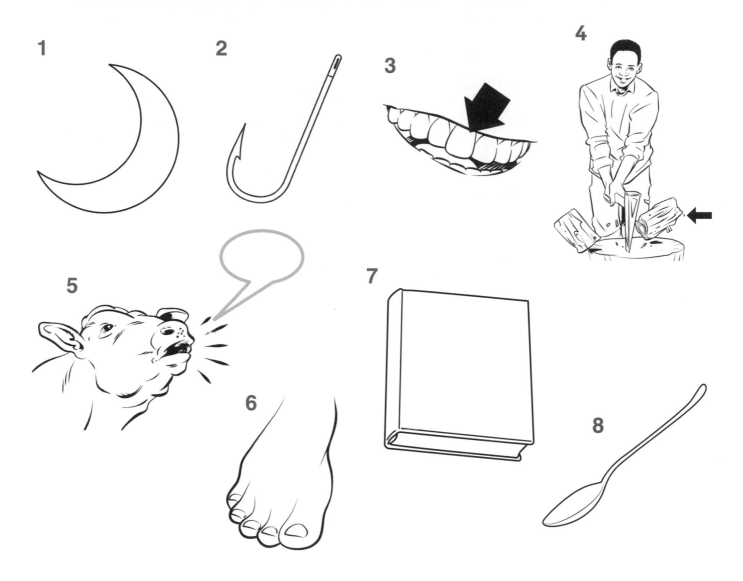

2 Use the pictures above to find the words to answer these riddles.

1 It is in my mouth. _____

2 A cow says this. _____

3 A chair is made of this. _____

4 I read a story in this. _____

Long vowel digraphs: 'ou' and 'ow'

1 Read the story aloud. Underline the words with 'ou'.
Put a ring round the words with 'ow'.

A mouse came to my house.

She jumped up and down.

She ran round and round.

She picked all my flowers.

Then she went to town.

2 Write the words in the correct box below.

'ow 'words	'ou' words
	mouse

3 Add more words to the box.

cloud

cow

owl

mouth

Long vowel digraphs: 'oy' and 'oi'

1 **Read the story aloud. Underline the words with 'oy'.**
Put a ring round the words with 'oi'.

Roy saw a toy car.

He pointed to the car.

Another boy had a coin.

He got the toy car.

Poor Roy.

2 **Write the words in the correct box below.**

'oi 'words	'oy' words
	Roy

3 **Find these words in the word puzzle. Draw a ring round them.**

e	d	o	i	l
n	o	i	s	e
j	m	u	h	g
o	b	o	i	l
y	v	j	o	y

oil
enjoy
noise
boil
joy

Section 2 Language

Nouns

1 Find at least four things in the classroom.
Write the nouns in the clouds.

pencil

2 Find at least four things at home.
Write the nouns in the clouds.

3 Use one of your nouns in a sentence.

_____

- Words which name things, people and places are called 'nouns'. Ask students to name things in the room (e.g. *chair, door, book*).
- Write the names of these things and tell students that the words are all nouns.

4 **Underline the nouns in these sentences.**

1 A <u>girl</u> went to a farm.

She saw a hen.

She saw a cow and a duck.

2 The bus stopped.

A lady got off.

A dog got off.

A man and a boy got on the bus.

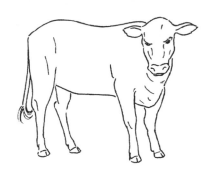

5 **Finish each sentence with a noun of your own.**

1 I like my _____.

2 My _____ is in my bag.

3 I can see a _____.

4 I like to eat _____.

5 I wish I had a _____.

Plurals: with 's'

1 **Write the word. Add 's' if there is more than one.**

> dog   car   ring   ball   bee   cat   jug

bees _____

ball _____

bee _____

_____ (jug)

_____ (dog)

_____ (ring)

_____ (car)

_____ (cat)

2 **Finish the sentences about you.**

I have one _____

and two _____.

I have ten _____

and two _____.

head

eye

finger

hand

• Tell students that 'plural' is another word we use for 'more than one'.

Plurals: with 'es'

1 **Draw more than one and write the plural with 'es'.**

final sound	one	more than one
ch	match	_____
sh	brush	_____
s	bus	_____
x	box	_____

2 **Show that there is more than one. Add 'es'.**

1  church_____

2 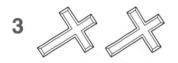 dish_____

3 cross_____

4  fox_____

- The rule is: add 'es' to words that end in 's', 'sh', 'ch', or 'x'.
- Draw attention to the fact that the plural of these words has two syllables.

Plurals: with 's' and 'es'

1 **Show that there is more than one. Add 's' or 'es'.**

arm   <u>arms</u>   lunch   _____

box   _____   duck   _____

goat   _____   crash   _____

cross   _____   book   _____

2 **Read this story.**
Write 's' or 'es' in the gaps to show there is more than one.

Dog and Pup went to have dinner with Tiger.

There were only two spoon____.

There were two glass ____ and two dish____.

There were lots of sandwich____ and drink____.

Tiger said, "I like to eat hot dog____."

Dog and Pup dropped their

fork____ and ran away.

'a' or 'an'?

Write 'a' or 'an'.

1
_an_ ice cream

2
_a_ cat

3
____ book

4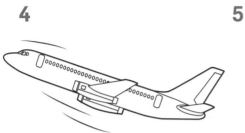
____ airplane

5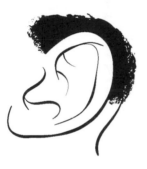
____ dog

6
____ umbrella

7
____ ear

8
____ table

9
____ egg

10
____ fish

11
____ apple

12 ____ hat

- Remind students that we use 'an' before a noun beginning with a vowel (a, e, i, o, u).
- We use 'a' before nouns beginning with all other letters.

Adjectives

1 **Write a word from the box to describe each thing.**

dirty	thin	fat	big	happy	black

1

a __fat__ cat

2

a _____ girl

3

a _____ shirt

4

a _____ baby

5

a _____ hat

6

a _____ tree

• Explain that some words tell us more about nouns, for example, the words 'big' or 'small'. These words are describing words or adjectives.

2 **Circle the words that describe the hats.**

an (old) hat

a small hat

a big hat

a dirty hat

3 **Draw two hats. Describe them.**

a _____ hat

a _____ hat

4 **Underline the describing words in the poem.**

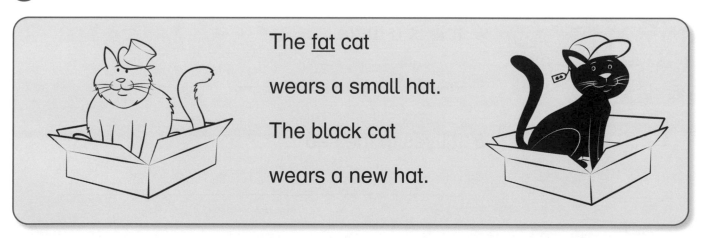

The <u>fat</u> cat

wears a small hat.

The black cat

wears a new hat.

5 **Write a poem of your own.**

The _____ cat

wears a _____ hat.

Sentences

1 These sentences need a capital letter and a full stop.
Write them out correctly.

1 this is a bird

This is a bird. _____

2 it is called a parrot

_____

3 birds can fly

_____

4 this is a turtle

_____

5 it lives in the sea

_____

6 turtles can swim

_____

• Remind students that a sentence begins with a capital letter and ends with a full stop.

2 **Sort the words in each sentence and write each one next to its picture. Put in the capital letters and full stops.**

1. planted   sam   a   seed

2. grew   flower   a

3. to   Mommy   it   he   gave

Sam planted _____

_____

_____

3 **Make up a title for this story.**

_____

4 **Are these sentences? Tick *yes* or *no*.**

	yes	no
a girl blue	☐	☐
I am six.	☐	☐
two dogs in	☐	☐
The boy has a cap.	☐	☐
My red is	☐	☐
This is my bag.	☐	☐

5 **Write a sentence about this picture.**

_____

_____

_____

_____

Capital letters

I live in Grenada.

1 **Answer these questions. Begin your answers with 'I'.**

1 How old are you?

I am _____ years old. _____.

2 Are you a girl or a boy?

_____.

3 Where do you live?

_____.

2 **Answer these questions.**
Use a capital letter to begin
names and months of the year.

My name is Justin.

My birthday is in August.

1 What is your friend's name?

My friend's name is _____.

2 What is your teacher's name?

_____.

3 Where do you live?

_____.

4 When is your birthday?

_____.

- Remind students that 'I' on its own is always a capital letter.
- Names of people and important places always begin with a capital letter.
- Days of the week and months of the year begin with capital letters.

Questions

1 Use question marks for the asking sentences.
Use full stops for the telling sentences.

What is your name __?__

My name is Anna ____

How old are you ____

I am six ____

Are you happy ____

Yes I am ____

That's Tom ____

Is he your friend ____

2 Write an asking sentence of your own.

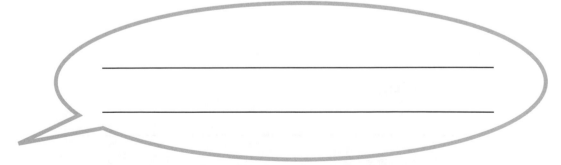

_____

_____

• Explain that a question is also a type of sentence, sometimes called an asking sentence. A question always begins with a capital letter and ends with a question mark.

3 Sort the words into a sensible question.
Finish each one with a question mark.

1   is your
friend Who

Who _____

2   is your ball
What colour

_____

3   like football
Do you

_____

4   my ball
Where is

_____

4 Write a question of your own.

_____

Punctuation

1 **Put full stops at the end of the telling sentences.**
Put question marks at the end of the questions.

1 This is my school____

2 Where is your school____

3 My teacher is Miss James____

4 Who is your teacher____

5 Do you like ice cream____

6 I like mangoes____

2 **Write a telling sentence about this picture.**

_____

3 **Write a question about the picture.**

_____

4 **Match the questions to the answers.**

questions	answers
Where did you live?	I liked Math.
What did you play?	Leo was my friend.
What did you like at school?	It was near to the Church.
Who was your friend?	I lived in Antigua.
Where was your school?	I played cricket.

5 **Put a full stop, question mark or exclamation mark at the end of each sentence.**

1 They play marbles____

2 Stop it____

3 Do you play marbles____

4 It's amazing____

5 I wear glasses____

6 We live in Barbados____

7 Go away____

Stop it!

• Explain that we use an exclamation mark after somebody shouts or says something surprising.

Verbs

1 **Write a list of things you can do.**
Use the words in the box or think of your own.

| run | bark | skip | hop | sleep |
| fly | eat | jump | cry | swim |

I can _____.

I can _____.

I can _____.

I can _____.

2 **Write two things a dog can do.**

A dog can _____ and _____.

3 **Write two things a frog can do.**

A frog can _____ and _____.

• Remind students that words that tell us what people do are called 'doing words' or verbs.

4 **What do you do in these places? Write two verbs.**

1 At school	**3** At home
I write _____	_____
_____	_____

2 At the beach	**4** In bed
_____	_____
_____	_____

5 **Underline the verb in each sentence.**

The girls sing.

The boys read.

Mom and Dad dance.

Grandma and I chat.

Verbs: *am*, *is* and *are*

1 **Fill in the gaps. Write *am* or *is*.**

1   This __is__ my family.

2   Mommy _____ on the left.

3   Daddy _____ on the right.

4   I _____ in the middle.

5   I _____ sitting on a gate.

2 **Fill in the gaps. Write *is* or *are*.**

The book _____ big.

The ball _____ small.

The book and the ball _____ on the table.

The cars _____ under the table.

Where _____ my bat?

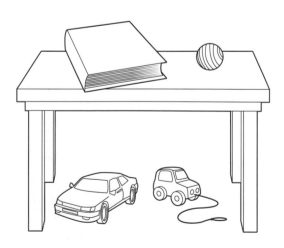

Verbs: *has* and *have*

1 **Finish the sentences using *have* or *has*.**

1 The nanny goat __has__ a boat.

2 Tabby cats _____ lots of hats.

3 Little mice _____ boiled rice.

4 The big cook _____ a book.

5 This mouse _____ a little house.

6 The slippery snake _____ a cake.

2 **Complete the sentences with *have* or *has*.**

1 I _____ a book.

2 You _____ a pencil.

3 She _____ a cup.

4 We _____ homework today.

5 They _____ assembly every day.

Verbs: present continuous

1 **What are these people doing?**
Finish the sentences.

playing	sleeping	fishing	cooking
	swimming	batting	

1 Daddy is _playing_.

2 Mommy is _____.

3 Grandad is _____.

4 The boy is _____.

5 The dog is _____.

6 The girl is _____.

2 **Draw a picture of you doing something. Finish the sentence.**

I am _____

_____.

• Tell students that when we say what someone is doing now, we add '-ing'. We use 'am', 'is' or 'are' as a helping word. For example: I *am* jumping, we *are* jumping, you *are* jumping.

3 **What are these children doing?**
Write the verb next to each picture.
Use the verb in a sentence.

| drinking | eating | fishing | running | watching |

1

running

The boy is running to school.

2

_____

_____

_____

3

_____

_____

_____

4

_____

_____

_____

5

_____

_____

_____

Verbs: present tense

1 **Complete these sentences. Use the correct verb.**

1 I ___move___ quickly. (move / moves)

A snail ___moves___ slowly. (move / moves)

2 I _____ in Antigua. (live / lives)

My cousin _____ in Belize. (live / lives)

3 We _____ on two legs. (walk / walks)

My cat _____ on four legs. (walk / walks)

4 He _____ meat. (eat / eats)

His cow _____ grass. (eat / eats)

5 I _____ painting. (like / likes)

She _____ painting. (like / likes)

We _____ painting. (like / likes)

• Tell students that the present tense tells us what happens usually.
• Sometimes we add 's' to the verb. For example *I / you / we / they walk* but *he / she / it walks.*

2 **Finish the sentences. Choose the correct verb.**

Every day Suzie _____ (get / gets) up early.

Her brothers _____ (get / gets) up late.

Suzie _____ (eat / eats) her breakfast and

_____ (brush / brushes) her teeth.

Her brothers _____ (jump / jumps) out of bed.

Then they (run / runs) out of the house.

3 **Write sentences about things you do every day.**
Use the pictures to help you.

Every day, I _____

_____

_____

_____

Verbs: *was* and *were*

1 **Cross out the word that is not correct.**

1 Anansi's wife was / ~~were~~ hungry.

2 His children was / were hungry.

3 Anansi was / were asleep.

4 His wife was / were angry.

5 She said, "You was / were asleep yesterday."

6 "I was / were at work."

7 Anansi said, "I was / were tired."

8 His wife said, "You was / were lazy."

2 **Answer these questions.**

1 Do you think Anansi was lazy?

   I think he _____

2 Do you think his children were happy?

   _____

• Explain that for things that happened in the past we use 'was' for one person or thing. The girl *was* tired.
• We use 'were' for more than one. The boys *were* tired. We also use 'were' after 'you'.

3 **Use *was* or *were* to finish each sentence.**

1 I ___was___ three years old.

2 My brother and I _____ in bed.

3 My mommy and daddy _____ in bed.

4 I _____ scared.

5 Two dogs _____ in the yard.

6 The moon _____ in the sky.

7 You _____ brave.

8 Mommy _____ kind.

4 **Change these sentences to the past tense.
Use *was* or *were*.**

1 Today I am happy.

   Yesterday I _____ happy.

2 Today you are at school.

   Last week you _____ at school.

Joining word: *and*

1 Join each pair of sentences using *and*.

1 My mom is tall. She is kind.

   <u>My mom is tall and she is kind.</u>

2 Mom runs. She reads.

_____

3 My dad is tall. He is funny.

_____

4 He drives a car. He rides a bike.

_____

5 We play football. We play cricket.

_____

6 Grandma has a dog. She has two ducks.

_____

7 We will have lunch. We will go to the beach.

_____

**2 This story has too many sentences.
Write it again. Join some of the sentences with *and*.**

Anna went to the store. She got some rice. She got some beans.
Then she came home.

_____

_____

- We use 'and' to join two sentences: We saw ducks. We saw a goat. → *We saw ducks and we saw goats.*
- When you join two sentences, you only need one capital letter (at the beginning of the sentence) and one full stop (at the end).

Joining words: *and* / *but*

1 **Join each pair of sentences using *but*.**

1 It is late. They are not tired.

  It is late but _____

2 We want to go out. It is raining.

  _____

  _____

3 She can dance. She can't sing.

  _____

  _____

2 **Make two sentences using *and*. Make two sentences using *but*.**

1 She ran to school		she was late.
2 She ran to school	and	it was good.
3 He ate some mango	but	she was on time.
4 He ate some mango		it was bad.

1 She ran to school and _____

2 _____

3 _____

  _____

4 _____

  _____

• Help students to see that the word 'but' introduces something that is different from the first part of the sentence, or something which might surprise us.

Prepositions: *in / on / under*

1 **Where is the dog? Finish the sentences with *in, on* or *under***

1  The pups are _____ the boat.

2  The pups are _____ the boat.

3  The pups are _____ the boat.

2 **Write a sentence about each picture.**

1  The puppy is _____

2  _____

3  _____

Prepositions: *behind / in front of*

1 **Where are they? Finish these sentences with *behind* or *in front of*.**

1  The boy is <u>behind</u> the car.

2 The cat is _____ the tree.

3 The dog is _____ the chair.

4 The girl is _____ the table.

5 The boy is _____ the tree.

6 The baby is _____ the television.

2 **Write three sentences about this picture.**

1 The tiger is _____

2 The parrot is _____

3 The monkey is _____

Environmental print

Where do you see these signs?
Write the words in the correct box.

Rhyme

1 **Say these words aloud. Join the words that rhyme.**

| leg | fun | hit | cat | cot |

| sun | peg | pot | bit | hat |

2 **Write a word that rhymes.**

cat _____

hot _____

lid _____

jug _____

beg _____

tap _____

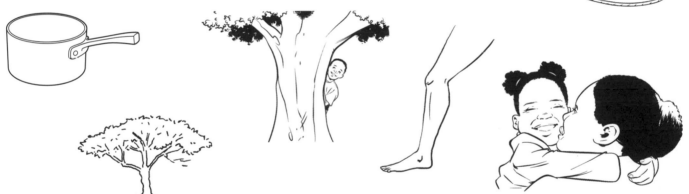

3 **Finish this rhyme. Use the picture to help you.**

The big fat _____.

Likes to sit on my _____.

4 **Think of words that rhyme with the word in bold type.**

big	fig		
tap			
pool			
fell			
pick			

5 **Colour in the words that rhyme.**

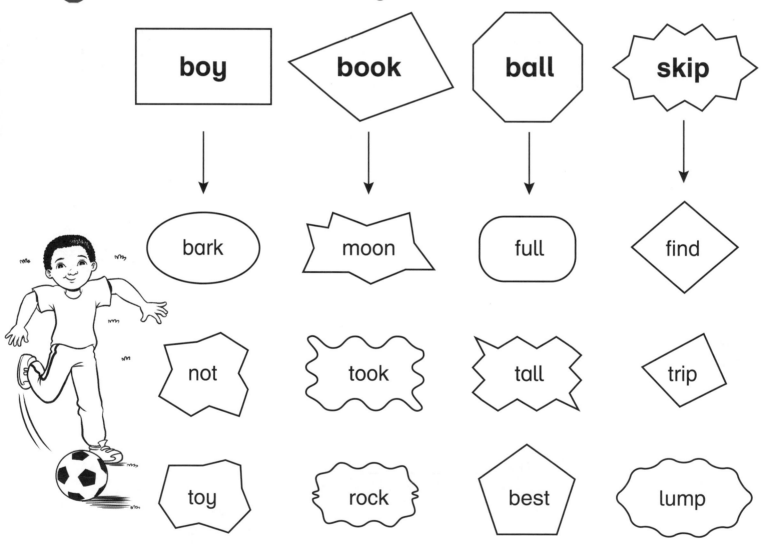

boy   book   ball   skip

bark   moon   full   find

not   took   tall   trip

toy   rock   best   lump

Compound words

1 Join two short words to make one long word.

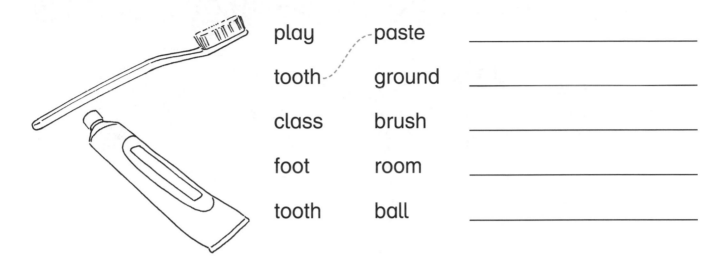

play	paste
tooth	ground
class	brush
foot	room
tooth	ball

_____

_____

_____

_____

_____

2 Choose two words. Use each one in a sentence.

1 _____

_____

2 _____

_____

3 How many compound words can you make from these words?

some   thing

+

no   body

_____   _____

_____   _____

4 **Join each of the words in wing 1 to a word in wing 2.**
Write the six new words

	1		2
1	butter	cake	
2	bed	spoon	
3	tea	fly	
4	gold	room	
5	hand	fish	
6	pan	bag	

1 _____   4 _____

2 _____   5 _____

3 _____   6 _____

5 **Choose two words. Use each one in a sentence.**

1 _____

_____

2 _____

_____

• Help students to see that some words are made up of two smaller words by covering one of the words
(e.g. *some* in *some*thing) and asking the child to read it before revealing the second part of the word.

Opposites

1 **Join each word to its opposite.**

big	dirty
old	sad
clean	fat
happy	small
thin	new

2 **Complete these pairs of opposites.**
Use a word from the box.

short	slow	soft	empty

full and
empty

long and
_____

fast and
_____

hard and
_____

3 **Match each word to its opposite**

1 good · · · · · · · · · · · poor

2 dry   new

3 hot   wet

4 rich · · · · · · · · · · · bad

5 old   cold

4 **Answer these questions.**

1   Is my hair wet or dry?

My hair is wet.

2   Is the dog clean or dirty?

_____

3   Is the door open or shut?

_____

4   Are my legs long or short?

_____

Synonyms

1 Colour in the word which has a similar meaning.

1 **shout**
 whisper
 mutter
 yell

2 **wet**
 dark
 damp
 empty

3 **fast**
quick
chilly
lose

4 **close**
meet
shut
try

2 Finish these sentences with a word that is similar to the word in bold.

1 **nice**   My friend is _____.

2 **little**   My cat is _____.

3 **big**   That hat is _____.

• Explain that 'similar' means almost the same. So, 'ancient' has a similar meaning to 'old'.

3 Look at the pictures and think of words you can use instead of *went*.

4 Write your words in the circle.
Add as many more words as you can.

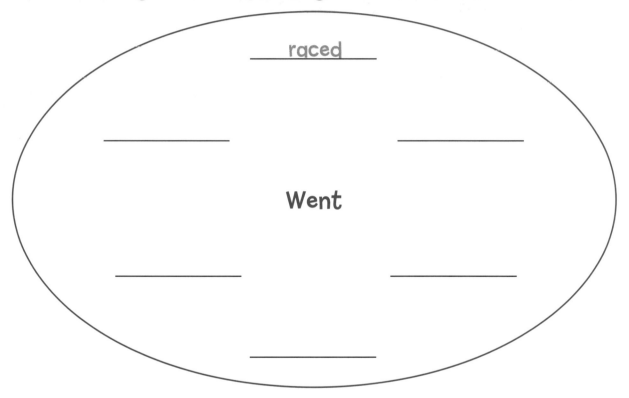

raced

Went

5 Choose two of the words you have written.
Use each one in a sentence of your own.

1 _____

_____

2 _____

_____

'wh' questions

1 **Join the question to the answer.**

Who is that lady?	It is on the table.
Where is she?	She is wearing a white coat.
What is she wearing?	She is talking to a patient.
What is she doing?	She is at the hospital.
Where is her laptop?	She is a doctor.

2 **Start each question with *Who, What* or *Where*.**

1 ___Who_____ is that man? He is my dad.

2 _____ is he going? He is going to the store.

3 _____ is he doing? He is driving a car.

4 _____ are those boys? They are my brothers.

5 _____ are they? They are in the car.

- We use question words to ask certain kinds of questions.
- 'Who' asks about a person. 'What' asks about a thing or things. 'Where' asks about a place.

Root words

1 **Look at these root words.**
Write other words in the word family by adding 'ing' and 'ed'

	-ing	**-ed**
help	helping _____	_____
pull	_____	_____
look	_____	_____
bang	_____	_____
sail	_____	_____
float	_____	_____

2 **Choose one of the words above. Use it in a sentence.**

_____

3 **Write each verb under its root word.**

pushing   painting   cooked   painted
cooking   pushed

push	**cook**	**paint**
pushed		

• Point out that we add a letter or letters to the end of a root word to change its meaning or to show that there is more than one. 'ing' tells us that something is happening now. 'ed' tells us that something happened in the past.

4 **Look at these root words.**
Write other words in the word family by adding 'ing' and 's'.

	-ing		-s
read	_____		reads _____
work	_____		_____
speak	_____		_____
wait	_____		_____

5 **Look at these word families. Write the root word in the box.**

playing   plays
plays

play

shouting
shouts   shouted

[ ]

talking   talks
talked

[ ]

jumping   jumps
jumped

[ ]

Alphabet

1 Which letters come before and after?

a b c d e f g h i j k l m n o p q r s t u v w x y z

1	r	s	t

2		b	

3		j	

4		f	

5		r	

6		v	

2 Write these nouns in alphabetical order.

mango

kite

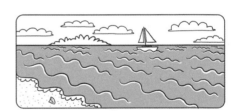

dog

bike

football

sea

1 bike _____

2 _____

3 _____

4 _____

5 _____

6 _____

Dictionary

1 **These words have to go in a dictionary.**
Do they go in the first or second half? Write each word
in the correct list.

> under   yam   big   girl   are
> kite   rain   wet   dirty   ~~see~~

the first half

a b c d e f g h i j k l m

_____

_____

_____

_____

_____

the second half

n o p q r s t u v w x y z

see _____

_____

_____

_____

2 These words are going in a picture dictionary.
Write them in alphabetical order.

a b c d e f g h i j k l m n o p q r s t u v w x y z

hen		**1** agouti
dog		**2**
rat		**3**
rabbit		**4**
mongoose		**5**
agouti		**6**
cow		**7**
goat		**8**
snake		**9**
pig		**10**

3 What do you think the picture dictionary is called?

An ABC of Flowers ☐

An ABC of Animals ☐

An ABC of Cats ☐

Sight vocabulary

1 **Circle the words that are the same.**

want	pant	⬭want⬭	wag	⬭want⬭
to	to	me	tip	to
my	my	man	my	be
do	do	dot	so	do
are	ant	car	are	are
one	one	new	out	one

2 **Sort out these sentences.**

1 a   bag.   I   want   new

_____

2 cake?   you   want   a   Do

_____

3 are   open.   stores   The

_____

4 to   Mom.   the book   gave   He

_____

• Exercise 2: Remind students that each of the sentences must begin with a capital letter and end with a full stop or a question mark. This will help them to sort out the mixed up words.

3 Put a ring around these words in the word puzzle.

r	w	a	s	g
o	h	e	a	p
w	e	n	i	t
u	b	w	d	h
h	a	v	e	e
s	h	e	c	y

was
said
have
he
she
they
we

4 Use one of these words to finish each sentence.

have   she   was

1 I _____ a sister.

2 _____ is called Grace.

3 Last week, she _____ not well.

4 _____ _____ sad.

5 "_____ a good sleep," I said.

6 _____ felt better soon.

7 I _____ decided to be a doctor!

Classifying

1 **Where do these things belong?**
Write them in the correct box.

toothbrush

cup

pot

shampoo

bathroom

toothbrush
_____
_____

kitchen
_____
_____
_____
_____
_____

spoon

dish

towel

fork

2 **Tick *yes* or *no*.**

	yes	no
We cook in the bathroom.	☐	☐
We brush our teeth in the bathroom.	☐	☐
We make dinner in the kitchen.	☐	☐

• Help students to see how things can be classified or put in groups. Write the word 'school' or 'beach' and ask them to suggest words that are related to it (*classroom, teacher,* etc).

3 You are going to the market and to the bookstore.
Make two lists using the items on the page.

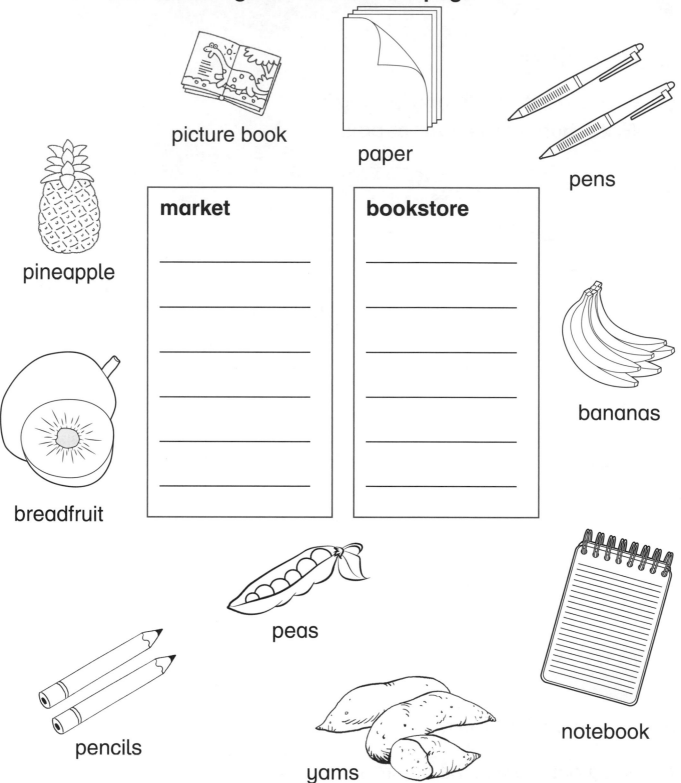

picture book

paper

pens

pineapple

breadfruit

market	bookstore
___	___
___	___
___	___
___	___
___	___
___	___

bananas

peas

pencils

yams

notebook

4 What else can you buy at the market or at the bookstore?
Add one more thing to each list.

Tell the story: story parts

1 **Number the pictures so that they tell the story.**

2 **Join the story part to the correct sentence.**

story part	sentence
Beginning	Kevin picked the beans.
Middle	Kevin gave the beans to his Mom.
End	Kevin watered the bean plant.

3 **What do you think happened next?**

_____

- Tell students that most stories have three parts: the beginning, the middle and the end.
- Re-read or retell them a story they know well. Together, work out which part is the beginning, the middle and the end.

Tell the story: pictures and words 1

1 **What is happening in the pictures?**

2 **Make up names for the boy, the girl and the dog.**

3 **Tell the story to a friend.**

• Do this exercise orally. Ask students to say what the boy might think and say when he hit the ball hard.

Tell the story: pictures and words 2

1 Retell the story on page 92.

2 What do you think the girl said to the dog?

 Bad dog!

 Clever dog!

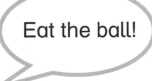 Eat the ball!

3 Write her words in the bubble.

4 Tick the best title for this story.

The Dog who Played Cricket ☐

The Big Game ☐

Tell the story: pictures and words 3

1 **Tell the story.**

2 **Who are the people in the story?**

1   two boys

2   a lady and a boy

3   a man and a lady

the characters

3 **Where does the story take place?**

1   school

2   town

3   bedroom

the setting

• Tell students that the place where the story takes place is called the setting.
• The people or animals in the story are the characters.
• Think of a story they know well. Together, work out who the characters are and where the story is set.

Tell the story: visual comprehension

1 **Look at the picture. Answer the questions.**

1 What is Daddy doing?

2 What is Mommy doing?

3 What is the boy doing?

4 Where is the hen?

5 What do you think will happen next? Draw what happens.

2 **Write each sentence under the correct picture.**

I went to the beach.

The house was on a hill.

They had lunch.

It was very windy.

_____

_____

_____

_____

Tell the story: literal comprehension

1 **Read about what Shera did yesterday.**

> Yesterday, I took my skipping rope to school. Iris wanted to skip with me. We skipped at playtime.

> At lunchtime we watched the boys play marbles.
> After school, I went to Sam's house. We watched television.

2 **Answer these questions with a sentence.**

1   What did Shera take to school?

   She took her _____

2   Who wanted to skip with her?

   _____

3   When did they skip?

   _____

4   Where did Shera go after school?

   _____

Tell the story: sequencing 1

1 **Number the pictures so that they tell the story.**

2 **Number the sentences in order.**

His sister got the cap out of the tree. ☐

It was windy. 1

It went into the tree. ☐

Tom's cap blew away. ☐

3 **Make up a title for the story.**

_____

• Sequence is the order in which things happen. Explain that, for us to be able to understand and enjoy a story, the events must be in the correct order.

4 **Re-read the story sentences on page 98.**
Are these sentences correct? Tick yes or no.

		yes	no
1	The boy's name was Tom.	☐	☐
2	The girl was his sister.	☐	☐
3	The girl had a cap.	☐	☐
4	It was windy.	☐	☐
5	It was raining.	☐	☐
6	The girl got the cap back.	☐	☐

5 **Make up answers to these questions.**

1 What was the girl's name?

_____

2 Where were they going?

_____

Tell the story: sequencing 2

1 **Number the pictures in the right order.**

2 **Number the sentences in order.**

The cat got wet. ☐

In the end, the cat ran away. ☐

She watered the plants. ☐

One day, Tessa filled the water can. 1

3 **Tell the story to a partner.**

Tell the story: sequencing 3

1 **Sort out the pictures to tell the story.**
Number them in the right order.

I am fast.
You are slow.
I will win the race.

FINISH

START

2 **Number the sentences in order.**

Hare went to sleep. ☐

Tortoise won the race. ☐

Tortoise went past hare. ☐

Hare ran very fast. Tortoise did not go fast. ☐

• These pictures tell the well-known fable *The Hare and the Tortoise*. With the students, talk through what happens in the story. Ask them to point to the words 'start' and 'finish' in the pictures.

3 **Which comes first? Number the pictures in order.**

1

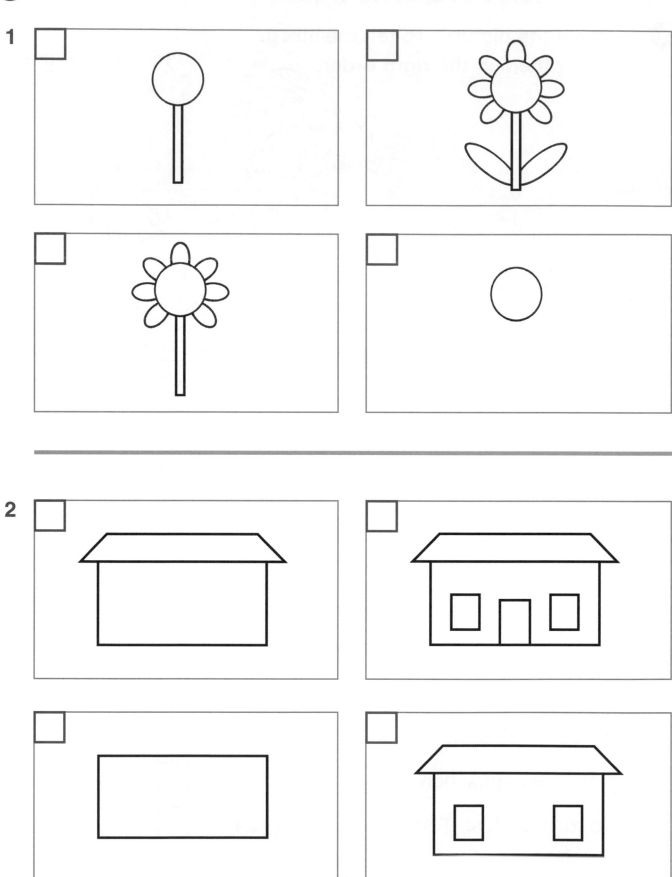

2

Tell the story: sequencing words

1 **Look at the pictures and tell the story.**

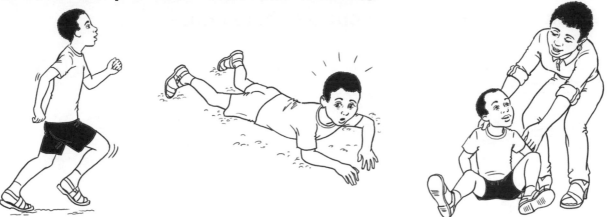

2 **Use one of these words to begin each sentence.**

Then	In the end	First

_____ Tom ran fast.

_____ he fell over

_____ his mommy came.

3 **Tell this story using these words.**

First	Then	In the end

• Explain that sequencing words help to give shape to our stories and accounts. They help the reader to enjoy and understand the story.

Tell the story: context clues

1 **Choose a word to complete the sentence.
Look for clues in the picture to help you.**

1 Tom and Anna are at the _____. (market / beach)

2 They are _____ ball. (playing / eating)

3 Anna wears a _____. (cat / hat)

4 Soon they will go _____. (swimming / painting)

5 Katya is in _____. (trouble / bed)

6 She is _____ book. (reading / writing)

7 It is _____. (daytime / night time)

8 Soon she will go to _____. (school / sleep)

• Tell students to look for clues in the pictures to help them read and understand. These are called 'context clues'.

2 **Choose a word to complete the sentence.**
Look for clues in the rest of the sentence to help you.

1   I read a good _____. (mango / book)

2   I painted a _____. (song / picture)

3   The _____ blew my hat off. (cat / wind)

4   That flower is a _____. (rose / house)

5   The _____ barked a lot. (rabbit / dog)

6   I _____ to school. (brush / walk)

3 **Choose a word of your own to complete the sentence.**
You will find clues in the title and in the words in bold.

On the Beach

We _____ in the **sea**.

We **played** _____ on the sand.

We **ate** _____ for lunch.

We **drank** lots of _____.

• Tell students to look for context clues in the rest of the sentence to help them read and understand.
• Ask which word gave them the clue? E.g. in Exercise 2, question 1, the word 'read' tells us that the answer is *book*.
• There is more than one correct answer to Exercise 3.

Section 4 *Comprehension* **105**

Tell the story: predicting

1 **Look at the pictures and tell the story.**

2 **What happened next? Draw a picture and write a sentence.**

- Exercise 1: Ask students to tell you what is happening in each picture. Then ask them to tell you the story.
- Exercise 2: When we are reading, we use clues from the picture and the text to predict or guess what may happen next. This helps us to read and to understand.

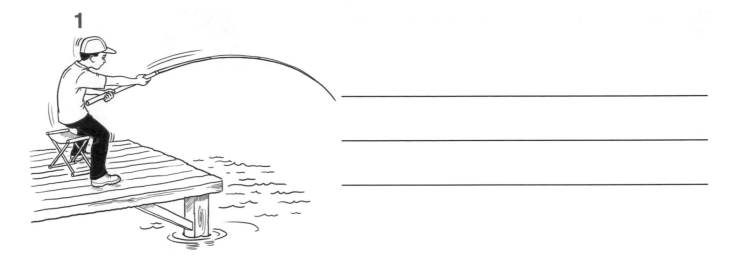

3 **What may happen next? Write a sentence.**

1

_____

_____

_____

2

_____

_____

_____

3

_____

_____

_____

Tell the story: inferring

1 **Match the words to the pictures.**

I am tired.

I am hungry.

I am angry.

I am thirsty.

I am sad.

I am happy.

2 **Danny broke his toy. How do you think he feels?**
Write a sentence.

_____

_____

- Explain that to 'infer' is to work out or to guess, based on the information we have. Often, when we are reading, we are given some information and are expected to work out the rest. We use clues from the picture and text. We also use our own experience. There is not always one correct answer to an inferential question.

3 Read what happened. How does each child feel?

1 Lisa left her lunch at home.

She also forgot her math book.

She wishes she had not come to

school today.

Lisa feels _____.

2 Darren got all the right answers

in the spelling test.

He smiles a big smile.

Darren feels _____.

3 Tia wants to sit next to Clara but

Clara does not want to sit next to Tia.

Tia feels _____.

4 Louisa is going to read a poem

at assembly.

She thinks she might do it badly.

Louisa feels _____.

• Discuss each of the situations with the child. Ask how they think they would feel if it happened to them.

4 **Read about how these children behave.**
What sort of person do you think each one is?

selfish   greedy   kind   clever   naughty

1 Leo helps his mother with the chores and he helps his grandma in her garden.

I think Leo is _____.

2 Nathan always takes the biggest piece of cake. He eats more chips than his big brother and sister.

_____

3 Stella hid her sister's toys. She threw her book out of the window.

_____

4 Maria always gets top marks in the math tests.

_____

Tell the story: main idea

1 **What is the best title for each of these pictures?**

1

a) The party
b) The holiday
c) The exam

2

a) Reading a book
b) Cooking
c) A new hat

3

a) Picking mangoes
b) Late for school
c) Climbing a tree

• Ask students to say what the picture is *about* (identify the main idea). This will enable them to choose the best title.

2 **What is each passage about? Underline the correct answer.**

1

> This is Ken.
> He is my brother.
> He is good at swimming.

a) swimming

b) Ken

c) brothers

2

> We painted a picture of fish. We painted big fish and small fish.

a) lots of fish

b) painting fish

c) eating fish

3

> Hummingbirds are very small. They have long beaks. They use their beaks to get food from flowers.

a) hummingbirds

b) beaks

c) flowers

• Tell students it is important to be able to say clearly what a story or passage is *about*. This is the main idea. Identifying the main idea is an important comprehension skill.

Understanding and inferring

1 **Read these riddles. Choose the correct answer from the box.**

1 I can fly.
I make a nest.
I lay eggs

What am I? _____

> a fish
> a mouse
> a bird

2 I have two wheels.
You can ride me.
I have brakes.

What am I? _____

> a car
> a bicycle
> a horse

3 I have four legs.
You can sit on me.
I am made of wood or plastic.

What am I? _____

> a chair
> a book
> a cushion

4 I am round.
People kick me.
People throw me.

What am I? _____

> a bat
> a cup
> a ball

Comprehension: fiction

1 **Read the story.**

> Anansi was hungry.
> He saw a mango tree and
> he took some mangoes.
> "Stop!" shouted Tiger.
> Anansi ran away.

2 **Answer the questions.**

1 Anansi was

   a) tired ☐   **b)** hungry ☐

2 What did Anansi see?

   a) a mango tree ☐   **b)** an orange tree ☐

3 What did Tiger shout?

   a) "Stop!" ☐   **b)** "Hello!" ☐

4 How did Tiger feel?

   _____

5 What do you think happened next?

   _____

   _____

• Questions 1, 2 and 3 in Exercise 2 are literal questions. The answers are clearly stated in the story.
  Students should tick the correct box.
• Questions 4 and 5 ask students for their opinion based on what happened in the story.

3 Read about Eldon.

Eldon is the tallest man in town.
He smiles at everyone in the street.
He plays with the children and
helps old people.

4 Answer the questions.

1 Eldon is

    a) tall ☐   **b)** short ☐

2 What does Eldon do in the street?

    a) he smiles ☐   **b)** he shouts ☐

3 What does Eldon do for the old woman?

    a) he helps ☐   **b)** he plays ☐

4 What sort of person is Eldon?

    a) a good person ☐   **b)** a bad person ☐

5 Why do you think that?

    I think Eldon is a good / bad person because _____

    _____

    _____

6 Would you like to meet Eldon? Why?

    I would / would not like to meet Eldon because _____

    _____

    _____

- Questions 1, 2 and 3 in Exercise 2, are literal questions. Students should tick the correct box.
- Questions 4 and 5 ask students for their opinion based on what they have read.
- Question 6 asks students for their own opinion and they can say yes or no, but they should explain their answer.

Comprehension: fiction or non-fiction?

1 **Read these book titles.**
Are they story books or information books?

		story	information
1	Birds and Butterflies	☐	☐
2	Anansi and the Yams	☐	☐
3	All about Farm Animals	☐	☐
4	How to Make Pancakes	☐	☐
5	Matilda Mouse Goes to School	☐	☐
6	The Cat who Flew	☐	☐

2 **Read these sentences.**
Are they from a story book or an information book?

		story	information
1	Mangoes grow on trees.	☐	☐
2	Barbados is an island.	☐	☐
3	The mermaid brushed her hair.	☐	☐
4	The boy lived under the sea.	☐	☐
5	Plants need water and sun.	☐	☐
6	The cow put on her best hat.	☐	☐

- Discuss with students the difference between things and events that are real and those that are not real.
- Ask if the characters and events in each title/sentence are real or not. For example, *Do cats fly? Do mangoes grow on trees?*

Comprehension: non-fiction

1 **Read about these animals.**

A rabbit has four legs.
It has long ears.
It has a small tail.

A parrot has two legs.
It has two wings.
It has feathers.

A fish has no legs.
It has fins.
It lives in the sea

2 **Answer these questions.**

1 What has feathers?

   A parrot has feathers.

2 What has long ears?

   _____

3 What has two legs?

   _____

4 What lives in the sea?

   _____

• Ask students whether these passages come from a story book or an information book.

3 **Read about starfish.**

> ### Facts about Starfish
> - Starfish live at the bottom of the sea.
> - Starfish have five arms.
> - A starfish has a mouth in the middle of the star.
> - Starfish eat small fish and clams.

4 **Does this passage come from a story book or an information book?**

5 **Which sentences are true? Which are not true?**

Remember:	
one starfish	two starfish

		true	not true
1	Starfish live on the beach	☐	☐
2	Starfish live in the sea.	☐	☐
3	Starfish have six arms.	☐	☐
4	Starfish have five arms.	☐	☐
5	Starfish eat plants.	☐	☐
6	Starfish eat small fish.	☐	☐
7	A starfish has a mouth.	☐	☐

- Explain that the plural of 'starfish' is also 'starfish'.
- Information text is often written in the present tense.

Comprehension: chart

1 **Read the school menu.**

School menu				
Monday	**Tuesday**	**Wednesday**	**Thursday**	**Friday**
rice and peas	macaroni pie	stewed chicken	beef roti	fried fish

2 **Complete the sentences.**

1 We had rice and peas on ___Monday___.

2 We had _____ on Thursday.

3 On _____ we had macaroni pie.

4 We had chicken on _____.

5 Which of these meals would you like best?

   _____

6 What do you have for lunch at school?

   _____

   _____

- Help students to 'read' the table. Introduce the word 'column'. Explain that the days of the week are headings and that the meal listed below the day is the one that is provided on that day.
- Remind students that the days of the week begin with a capital letter.

Comprehension: instructions

1 **Read what the teacher says to the class. Tick the instructions.**

1   Stand up.

2   Where is Stefan?

3   This is your book.

4   Sit down.

5   Put your books away.

6   Is a bee an insect?

7   Open your books.

8   Good morning.

2 **Which instructions would you use?**

Put on your hat.   Stop fighting.

Read the poem aloud.   Don't run.

1   <u>Stop fighting.</u>

2   _____

3   _____

4   _____

3 **What instruction would you give this girl?**

_____

_____

Comprehension: poem

1 **Read this poem.**

My Neighbours

Mr. Hall is very tall.
Mrs. Hall is very small.
Mr. Pratt is very fat.
Mrs. Pratt wears a hat.

Mr. Gold is very old.
Mrs. Gold is very bold.
Mr. Brown wears a frown.
Mrs. Brown is upside down.

by Leonie Bennett

2 **Make up actions to go with the words.**

3 **Answer the questions.**

1 What is the title of this poem? _____

2 Who is small?
   a) Mr. Pratt ☐   b) Mrs. Hall ☐

3 Which word describes Mr. Gold?
   a) old ☐   b) tall ☐   c) bold ☐

4 Find three words in the poem that rhyme with 'town'.
   _____   _____   _____

5 Is this poem
   a) serious? ☐   b) funny? ☐

- Explain that the poet is the person who wrote the poem.
- Ask students if they like the poem and why. Which is their favourite line?

4 **Read this poem.**

I have two hands
Left and right.
They can throw and catch
And hold things tight.

I have two eyes
Left and right.
They can see in the day
But not at night.

by Leonie Bennett

5 **Make up actions to go with the words.**

6 **Answer the questions.**

1 How many verses are there in this poem?

a) one ☐ b) two ☐

2 How many lines are there in each verse?

a) four ☐ b) two ☐

3 Find three words in the poem that rhyme with *light*.

_____ _____ _____

4 What is the best title for this poem?

a) My hands ☐ b) My hands and eyes ☐

c) Throw and catch ☐

5 What else can you do with your hands?

_____

• Explain that poems are often divided into verses. Each verse or group of lines is separated from the next by a line space.
• To decide the title, ask students to think what the poem is about (main idea).

Section 5 Writing

Write about yourself

Answer each question with a sentence.

1   What is your name?

My name is _____

2   Where do you live?

I live in _____

3   What school do you go to?

_____

4   What games do you like to play?

_____

_____

5   What do you like to eat?

_____

_____

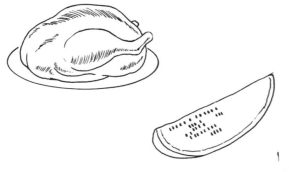

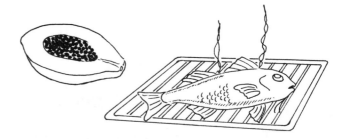

Write a story

1 **Tell the story. Write a sentence next to each picture.**

> boy   tree

_____

_____

> fell   hurt   knee

_____

_____

> Mommy   washed

_____

_____

2 **Now write the sentences in this chart.**
What happens at the beginning, in the middle and at the end?

1 Beginning	_____
2 Middle	_____
3 End	_____

3 **Write a sentence next to each picture to tell the story.**
Use the words under the picture to help you.

girl   had   kite

_____

_____

let   go

_____

_____

ran   after

_____

_____

4 **What do you think happened next? Write a sentence.**

_____

_____

5 **Look at the picture. Talk about the questions with a friend. Use your answers to help you to make up a story.**

1 Who is this boy?

2 What is in the box?

3 Where is he?

4 What happens next?

6 **Write a story about the boy in the picture.**

_____

_____

_____

_____

_____

• Encourage students to suggest more than one thing that might be in the box in the picture and to talk about what the boy is going to do with it. Who lives in the house? Remind students that a story has a beginning, middle and end.
• The picture is the beginning of this story.

Write an account of a personal experience

1 **Draw a picture of what you did at the weekend.**

2 **Now write about what you did at the weekend.**

Where were you?

I _____

_____

What did you do?

_____

_____

When did you do it?

_____

_____

How did you feel?

_____

_____

3 **Think about something that happened which made you happy.**

4 **Tell your friend about it. Use these questions to help you.**

- When was it?
- Where were you?
- Who were you with?
- What happened?

5 **Write about what happened in the order in which things happened.**

_____

_____

_____

_____

_____

- The questions should help students to remember details of what happened. They can also draw a picture on another sheet of paper to help them to remember.
- Remind students to use 'I', 'me' and 'my' when writing about themselves.

Write a description of a thing

1 **Circle the words that describe the puppy in the picture.**

cute

small

enormous

dangerous

playful

2 **Imagine stroking the puppy.**
Circle the words that describe how it would feel.

hard

warm

furry

soft

cold

3 **Complete the sentence using some of the describing words.**

I played with a _____ puppy.

4 **Circle three words that describe a ripe mango.**

sweet

yellow

hard

sour

blue

soft

5 **Complete the sentence using two of the describing words.**

I ate a _____ mango.

- Tell students that using describing words helps to make writing more interesting. It helps to give the reader a vivid picture of the thing the writer is describing.

Write a description of a person

1 **Draw a picture of someone you know well.**

2 **Describe your person.**

1 What does he or she look like?

_____

_____

2 What sort of person is he or she?

_____

_____

3 What does your person like to do?

_____

_____

• Explain that to bring a description 'to life' they should say what the person does and how they behave, not just what they look like.

Write a description of a place

1 Think of a place you know well.
Write the name of your place in the circle.

I can see

_____

_____

I can hear

_____

_____

My place

_____

Words that describe my place

_____ _____ _____

2 Write what you can see and hear when you are at your place.

3 Write sentences about the place you have chosen.

_____

_____

_____

_____

• Encourage students to use their senses when they are describing a place. They may also be able to say what they felt, tasted or smelt in the place they are describing.

Write information

1 **One of these sentences is a fact.**
Put a circle round the fact sentence.

A cow has four legs.   A cow can fly.

2 **Write a fact about each of these things.**

1

A car has _____.

2

A house has _____.

3

A shirt has _____.

4

A chair has _____.

5

A bicycle has _____.

6

A cat has _____.

- Remind students that facts are true statements. 'My hat is blue' and 'Antigua is an island' are facts.
- The statements 'Blue is nicer than red' and 'Antigua is the prettiest island in the Caribbean' are not facts. They are opinions.

3 **Choose an animal. Draw a picture of it.**

4 **Write the name of your animal in the circle. Write three facts about it.**

1 _____

2 _____

My animal

_____

3 _____

5 **Write sentences about your animal.**

_____

_____

_____

_____